Revenge of the "Illegal Alien:"

A Mexican Takes on the Emp

Poetry, Short Stories & Political Bullets

By **César A. Preciado-Cruz** (teolol)

A Making Changes Publication

Making Changes Press, Oakland, CA.

Revenge of the "Illegal Alien:"

A Mexican Takes on the Empire

Making Changes Press

PO Box 27231 Oakland, CA. 94602

www.CesarCruz.com

Printed in Aztlán

Cover design by author.

ISBN: 978-0-6151-5299-8

Library of Congress Control Number: 2008901057

this book is dedicated to my wife, Jazmín,

i am blessed to walk with you on this path…

written for our son, Santiago Olin,

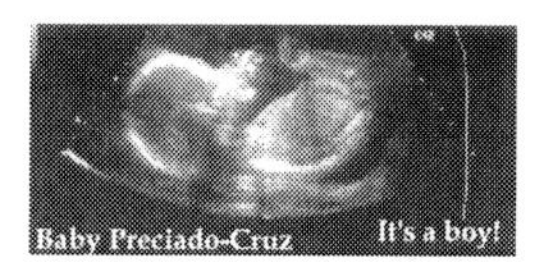

with the pen and ink of my entire familia,

and inspired by all people who struggle for freedom,

onamove.

gracias

madre te doy las gracias por darme vida y por luchar tanto por mi, **abuelita**-gracias por toda tu sabiduría y tu amor. **marcos**-gracias por ser como un padre para mí. hermanita y hermanito (**jessica y joshua**)-siempre estoy orgulloso de ustedes, los amo mucho. **jazmín**-gracias por todo tu amor, por caminar este camino conmigo, siempre me inspiras, te amo…**santiago olin**-esto es para ti, encuentra tu voz y ¡no te dejes! **familia preciado-**gracias por aceptarme como uno de ustedes. **familia de juchitlán**-como los extraño, gracias por darme raíces. **abuelito**-gracias por tus consejos, se que desde el cielo sonríes.

thank you

before i begin know that if i forget to thank you, please blame it on the head (my terrible memory), but not on the heart, because i am forever grateful. **mikey & joe**-thank you 4 rollin', i pray 4 u and wish you the best, **dr. tepper**-thank you for challenging me, **stacy**-thank you for keepin' it real, **sherry**-thank you for introducing me to 'taiwan,' **israel (izzy)**-thank you for your humor & for fasting 26 days (we did it), **yaocihuatzin**-thank you for trying to find you, and helping me find me, stay on that 'red road,' **profe taylor**-thank you for pushing me to not see you as white, but as human, you have a great heart, **norwalk christian family**-thank you for giving me a chance & for showing me *The Word*, **comité downer**-thank you for standing up for your rights, **downer poets**-you inspire me to write, keep at it, **wayne & christina**-thank you for opening your home and heart to us, you are both blessings from the most High (welcome home **junobi**), **making changes freedom school family**-dream and don't let anyone stand in your way, so they shut down the building, but never the movement, **mike & ivonne**-keep achieving but don't forget 2 give back, **osos family**-keep takin' on those frats and sororities (smash, but also build), **nsurgentes**-our work is not done, i believe in you, believe in yourselves and change the world, **eoc & avenues crew**-so they closed the building, let's grind (8 miles and still got 1 to go), **oakland leaf/upa family**-like the *phoenix* we are rising, **my lifelong students** (2 many 2 name)-i love you, take what you learned and find your calling, it's time to shine, **end-dependista poets-**your voices still echo in my heart (keep writing and inspiring), **la onda bajita crew & kpfa family-**speak truth to power even if they take you 'off' the air, **gavilan**-thank you maestro 4 always teaching, **sal (brownpride)**-thank you for giving my voice an audience when no-one else would, **c.i.g.**-thank you for helping me grow, **yellow rage/ paris/ yuri kochiyama/ brent beltran/ luis rodriguez/ profe acuña-**thank you for your kind words, you all inspire and motivate me to keep writing… last but not least, **Great Spirit**-given so many names, thank you for life, for all these people i have been blessed to meet, they give me hope, thank you for the sun, moon and stars, another wor(l)d is possible, we need not be in despair because your song-writer **bob marley** said, 'none of [these evil doers] can stop the time…' thank you for letting me find my role; *to comfort the disturbed and to disturb the comfortable.* Let's do it then.

We are the New Voices

preface poem

"We are the new voices
on a move
finding space between
silence and insanity
we scream stopping rapists
and inspiring introverts
to express and be heard

We are the new voices
that chuck d airs with a rebel yell
there is no mute button
    no silencer to stops us
and unlike duracell™
we don't need replacements

We are the new voices
carrying chants
from Orishas and Abuelas
rolled under our tongue

We spit consejos
like the u.s gov. does soldiers

We are truth sayers
with no time to fake da' funk
creating invisible codices
that need audiences time
to press rewind
to decipher their messages

we make you say
"what?" and "come again!?"
"did you feel that cat?"
"They bringin' it tonight!!"

Them new voices
on a move
angry and hopeful
givin' birth
deconstructing lies and history

Them voices are hope
amidst the rage of the storm
taking on political hurricanes
and empires to boot

WE are the new voices
with an ear to the griots
and grandpas
speaking their worldview
through our mouths
our eyes
and our fists

We are the new voices
that can't be silenced
and yes
were ***onamove***..........

. . .

Revenge of the "Illegal Alien:"

A Mexican Takes on the Empire

Table of CONtents

Poemas en Español

Commentaries

Closing

soy

I am Mexica(n) prince
often mislabeled a *"messy' can"*

I am
Salvatrucha
Nicaragüense
Hondureño
Guatemalteco and so much more
but people can't seem to find my countries on a map

I am from this land
california Aztlán Anahúac
but to you, I'm an immigrant
an illegal alien
your wetback

I hear I take 'your **jobs**' »»»»» and yet we do the jobs you won't do

I hear I '***don't speak*** *English so good*' »»»»» **but we speak** english,
spanish, Nahuatl, Quechua
and Caló all with one tongue

I hear I'm '**lazy**' taking *'siestas'* and all »»»»» yet **I work harder** in a day
than most do in a week

I hear 'I'm the **problem**' »»»»» but I'm always droppin'
solutions

I hear 'I'm the **criminal**' »»»»» and yet **you stole** our land

I am Mayan/Inca royalty
with a name you still butcher and can't pronounce
and no I'm not tacos or nachos
I am pyramids and mathematics

while you were still living in caves in the dark ages
I've been graffiti's grandparents
inspiring hieroglyphs

I am norte and sur
with no need for a green card

I am at least 4 directions
worthy of more than just your respect

Y eso es quien soy

(translate it your d--n self)

. . .

license this

i am those illegals   you despise
i am the unwanted   you hate

but maybe, to you, i'm in disguise   or incognito
somehow it's ok when you're trying to pick us up
for a bargain outside of **Home Depot™**
to build your new deck
or touch up your house

it's quite fine if we pick your overpriced fruits & vegetables
(for your organic grocer)
but pay us measly starvation wages

it's alright if we cook your crème brûlée
or bus your table
even if we wipe the shit from your kids' asses
but when we want licenses
"what nerve?!"   *"don't they know their place?"*

but see were not asking anymore
you can take your jobs and shove 'em

we're organizing and learning your language
while keeping ours
we haven't bought into all your lies
even if you repackage them
with coconut his-panic salesmen

we're organizing and we have no vanguard
moms are on the frontlines
en la vecindad saying to the governor

'sacaremos a ese buey de la barranca'
and we know what's comin'
like South Africa
a minority ruled
apartheid a part lie
sponsored by the rich white side
so too here in kkkalifornia
where the only thing real is
the uncovering of your lies

our struggle is not about licenses, or sb-60,
it's about reparations
for you're on our land and rent's way overdue
now tonantzin tecumseh and tupac
are all gettin' ready to collect their due

so go ahead call me illegal
even though i'm Mexican on Mexican land

call me wetback
you're no longer in a position of power
as you hide behind minuscule positions and cower
when we confront your tactics as a liar-liar

watch us organize & cripple your economy
as we boycott every corrupt multinational in sight
you don't stand a chance
and you can't hide in the suburbs no more
cuz we're comin' & runnin'& gunnin' to get ya
and the boat home is
already gone.

...

There's A Place

Dedicated to Juchitlán, Jalisco, México

there's a place
where a roosters crow
serves as local alarm clock
education comes while
milking an overprotective cow
who'll strike you
if you approach her child

there's a place
where Catholic saints come alive
and the holy ghost gives
grandma's arthritis
entire days off

there's a place
where grandpa
works another man's land
and still smiles after 16-hour days

there's a place
on an unpaved road called memory
where having "nothing"
becomes a blessing.

and in that place
callous hands salt tortillas
and Holy Ghost believers crawl
adorned with crowns full of thorns

somewhere in that place
a man forgets I.N.S. (I.C.E.) '*migra*' raids
television's hypnotic rays
and the constant spit in the face
for being broke and uneducated

that place
where roosters crow
cows protect their young
and hope grows faster than weeds
I once called
home.

can you translate this?

can you translate lines on a map
guarded by M-16s?

how would you say "*qué*
nos quieren dividir pa' matarnos," in English?

what is the correct spelling for death squads
so the u.s. papers will finally print it right?

in what grammatical tense shall we speak of
los *desaparecidos*?

and can you spell-check or do a word count
on how many paragraphs it takes to describe a
mother grieving on a casket
after her child has been tortured repeatedly for days
testicles chopped off
his eyeballs forked out
mailed to her home
so that she can see
that it doesn't pay to witness
federales *judiciales*
and CIA *oficiales*
exercising 'democracy'
in his backyard as they ram their dicks
up his little sister…

how
do you translate that?

. . .

To the teacher, social worker, politician, and critic who wonder why People of 'Color' continue to be disadvantaged.

I WONDER

You wonder why I drink, do drugs, steal, rob and kill?

You wonder why I don't care about your opportunities?

You wonder why I won't enlist in the SERVICE?

You wonder why I drop out of high school?

You wonder why I'm always in jail?

You wonder why I'm always pregnant?

You wonder why I'm always poor?

I wonder why there's a liquor store on every block in my neighborhood.

I wonder why the CIA would have a vested interest in keeping me
addicted to crack.

I wonder why if I steal a slice of pizza I get life imprisonment,
and if you're **ENRON™** and you steal 1.9 billion dollars you get a pardon.

I wonder why after 200 years of white male preferential treatment YOU have the nerve to tell ME to stay in school, and yet eliminate affirmative action.

I wonder why they continue to teach me that Lincoln freed the slaves,
and Columbus discovered America.

I wonder why they refuse to teach me my own history.

I wonder why poor Blacks and Chicanos are receiving preferential treatment in America's prisons.

I wonder why my people pay a higher percentage of taxes,
while you receive tax incentives.

I wonder why 'news at 11' had my mother as the top story as a 'welfare queen,' when we all know that the largest recipients of welfare are your corporations.

I wonder how it is that you have the nerve to question why I'm poor,
uneducated, in jail, drunk, or on crack.

I wonder how it is that you even blame me for the problems that you created.

I wonder? I wonder, don't you?

. . .

if the dead could speak

upon arrival
i stick out like a sore thumb
and i'm told my place after reading Newsday™
which speaks of the beat down
in Riverhead, Long Island
or any city
where you walk   while Mexican

upon arrival
your stares   cut me   stab me
puncture my pride
but i do not hide or disguise
my identity

do 2 day laborers, *jornaleros*,
scare you that much
that one day   after our screams
for independence
you decide to call your buddy Ryan and say,
"Let's do this!?"

how did you come
to plan   to pick up 2 Mexicans?

how did you come to plan a drive
to an abandoned building in Shirley
or for that matter any town?
          to even find
an abandoned building
in the first place?

how did you come to plan to acquire
wooden 2x4s and knives
only to hide them and use them
stabbing and penetrating
the sweaty backs of 2
    Mexicans   as you hammered
copper nails into their
vertebrates 'til the bleeding
drenched completely
your new shoes?

how did you come
to plan and believe
your 'christian' plot
to kill fellow children of god
as you claim
'christian identity'
as your reason for stabbing and beating a
wetback and greaser into I.C.U.?

how did you come
to believe that
their mother is different from yours?
that their father
doesn't feel what yours feels?

how did you come to
hide them and commence to
beat the living daylights
out of these 2 innocent men
'til they bled to death?

and what part of Christ
did you follow
on that day?

how did you come
to hate so much
that you despise
my skin?
my people?
my life?

if the dead could speak,
how would you explain to them
that you despise
wetbacks so much that
you would justify murder?

how did you come to hate me?

here
are the shadows of the dead
you butchered
confronting you
now
we are in your sleep
your shadow
following your every move
wondering
how you live
with so much hatred
in your heart?

. . .

I'm sick

I'm sick

constantly throwing up **cnn™** infomercials

that paint american soldiers

as liberators of yet another part of the world

I'm tired of people in suits behind desks

lying to me every hour on the hour

and my own family backing them up

deep down

I know george bush ain't my savior

but with enough TV and print ads

they now call news

I'm beginning to think otherwise

I never hear or see

the U.S. dropping bombs on hospitals

and mutilating children but they do

I never hear the c.i.a assassinating revolutionaries

but constant funerals without processions

speak otherwise

I am *though*

inundated with army-of-one commercials

and marines propaganda telling me

I too could be another superhero

If I climb the highest mountain

fight the dragon

take my rifle and turn it into a sword

and destroy my enemy

now I don't know about you

but I haven't seen too many dragons
in my neighborhood *'cept*
maybe the tax collector after every april 15th
and if u miss a payment
they'll come at you with more than just fire

american soldiers   recruiters   news agencies
government officials   teachers   politicians
LIE   time and again

they even recommend the army for kids gone astray
a training boot camp
that's the solution
turn kids into murderers
and when they come back from fighting your war
dump 'em on the streets
but hey   at least they'll salute you
won't speak out of line
won't question anything
and they'll continue bowing down
"yes sih, no sih"
and slavery can continue

I'm sick
can't go anywhere
can't see anything
can't read anything
without their propaganda asking me to join
their army   their lies   their madness
and I wonder for how much longer
I'll have a choice
and if I even have one now

...

Lobby #3

Teolol
Indigenous foreigner
in an american museum
stares at janitors
who remind him
of mexica goddesses

codices from guatemala
on display
in glass cases
as children
take snapshots
of "lost" civilizations
found in lobby #3

the tour continues
on the western wing
where northern indian figurines
of geronimo and pocahontas
speak
at the press of a button
they tell their story
of harmony and mother earth
to adults in cotton
"save the environment"
t-shirts

Teolol
stands at odds
amidst images
displays and artifacts
that remind him
he's a foreigner
in an American museum
where he must pay
the six-dollar entry fee
to see his ancestors
in lobby #3

...

burryin' trick-hop™

people wonder why i act a fool
but my only role models tell me that my
milkshake brings all the boys to the yard™

so i guess they just want us to
shake that thing™
as long as we don't question what education
tea- chers bring

see black & brown history
in schools is still a mystery

in the old school we weren't just bumpin' **lodi-dodi™**
we were buildin' with the black panther party
& it wasn't about ***"pass the bacardi***™"

see life's not about da' ***'bling bling™'***
but someone is trying to pull our strings
making us worship
nike™ & **hillfigga™**
talkin' about is you fitted?
nah brotha is you wit' it?
see they chargin' us $150 for air **jordans™**
when the workers who made them get a buck-fifty
so who's getting' rich
pimpin' us like they're our **trickdaddy™?**
making us believe that hiphop is about our clothes
and not our culture
about our **ice™** and not our roots

are you **mos(t) def™?**
cuz to them you're worth less than **50cent™**

and **busta™** your **rhymes** are tired
what you're tellin' me is straight **ludacris™**
no-torious™ lies

you speak of **g** **-unit™**
but what you know about thee u- nion
of people fightin' for freedom

(nelly™)
you think a grown man with a band-aid is cute?
try grown men in body bags
try this state building 23 new prisons
and not a single new college?
bump that on the radio
while you singin' and actin' a fool
the governator is walkin' all over u

they tryin' to get us to ***shake that thing™***
milkshaking™ that ass straight to prison
and it's **clear™** what **channel™** is gonna get
"our head sprung" ™
gonna get our head hung

plastic tired trick-hop
wanna-be corporate **gangstaz™**
making us believe life's about the size of your crib
half-naked women and what u **floss™**
little man while your future is gettin' tossed
but go 'head and tune in to **K-M-E-L™**
while our people are still catchin' hell
cuz' on **mtv™** & **bet™** they still have our people on s[illegible]

but i guess as long as it's got a bumpin' beat
and it's 4 da street
we're gonna yell less than a ***tweet tweet*™**
cuz' they straight think our movement is hella' weak

so where do u stand wit' that?
you gonna let 'em play u like u wuz' on crack
while ur culture is getting' jacked
and our people are under attack
nah sisters and brothers I can't bump that
you betta' take that (fill in the blank**™**) CD back

it's time to march
& more than just **8mile(s)™**
this is the reeducation
of not just **lauryn hill™**
and it is **common™** that **mystik journeymen™**
who carry **roots™** and are planning the **coup™**
are **public enem(ies)™** to **dead prez™** and alive ones 2
cuz **kanye™**
should not just be a fad in the **west™**
as we reclaim **aztlán™**
that's moving beyond the **underground™**
so go ahead and bump that on the radio
but stay low from the **popo™**
and in the **eve™**
keep ur eye on the **blackstar™**
as the funeral for this here **trickhop™**
and the resurrection of the truth in hiphop
is coming

. . .

on the 4th u lie (4th of july)

on this 4th of july
you tell more than just 4 lies
claiming you brought democracy to iraq
yet all they've seen is body bags
as you jack
their oil   their lives
and at home tell us
red   white   &   blue lies

it must be easy
making everyone pledge allegiance
from kinder to 12th grade
while recruiting killers in preschool
with army dot com™ videogames
you gettin' desperate
and we know it

see on this 4th of july
we can see through your lies

you play patriot games with Americans
making us believe that our vote matters
when democrat or republican
the rich run the country
while the poor die defending it

america needs poverty   and wants poverty
america needs homelessness   and wants homelessness
america yearns for skid row   and needs skid row
cuz' without it
there wouldn't be people

desperate enough to take anything you dish out
and not revolt

we would be desperate enough
to live in slums
to eat out of trashcans
to work to be a slave
to be in debt to visa™
to be the prostitute of the i.r.s. ™
to accept crumbs
to be a second class citizen
or even an illegal alien

to kill in your name
to die in your name
to be a slave in your name
but not in my name

see america
on this 4th of july
we can see through ur' lies
and no matter how pretty is the disguise
or how high the fireworks rise
i pray and build for your demise

i say it again
i pray and build for your demise
and ultimately for the truth to rise
that's what will remain
after the smoke clears
from your patriotic disguise

. . .

just pledge

i bled allegiance
was shot and dragged
in the united states of amerikkka

i lived repression
for which this country stands
one nation,
under martial law
indivisible,
with slavery,
and cheap labor for all

...

my vote

yeah I'm looking to vote
for the one who will
tear down the border

for the one who will
not treat human beings
like rabbits at hunting season

for the one who will
actually throw white collar criminals in prison
starting with him or herself

for the one who is not branded by nike™ or haliburton™

for the one who will not regulate who I am,
my body, who I marry, how I live

for the one who does not sell-out
to the highest bidder

but I guess that's wishful thinking
cuz democrats/republicans
at the top
sell themselves daily
no one stands for anything
except status & power

both want war
both believe that others
are the terrorists

and not themselves

so i guess i have a lot to learn
about north american democracy
where the choices are little to none
where the lesser of two evils
is what i should rally around

so excuse me if i'm not
jumping for joy this election
when the country says
it has no money for schools
but plenty for prisons
when the country can't fund an after-school program
but has billions for stealth bombers

me the noncitizen
i'm voting daily
with my voice my pen
my life and my fist
i'm not tripping about nov. 2nd
i'm building for the hereafter
and this economy can only remain strong
as long as we comply

what happened to no taxation without representation?
there's no need to fear this government
cuz *"it can't stop the time"*

so yeah vote everyday
don't let 'em silence
your opinions your expression

expose   what you see
what they don't see
what they won't see
what they won't tell
            otherwise
we'll be left believing
the false hope of this election
these candidates
this trickster democracy
            as our only way   as *thee* american way
when it is merely one way
that they attempt to keep us in the dark

so I do vote
            I cast my ballot for the light
shinin' like a *sendero luminoso*
            in the darkness of amerikkka
shinin'
            even if we pay no pg&e™ bill
shinin'
            exposing your lies
                        creating another way
            like sunrays bringing forth a new day
shinin'
            cuz it's time,

            and amerikkka,
you can't stop or misplace our votes
cuz we' shinin!'

. . .

"**Propositional Politricks**"

so many things have not been said
it's never been about proposition
187, 184, 21, 54 and/or fill-in-the-blank

it's not about saying "no"
not about someone else dictating
what students on campus organize around
and then come election day
we get all depressed
because it passed
it's not about that

it's not about the oakland p.d. ™
the oakland riders
acquitted of murder and brutality
when the people face a different reality

it's not about an actor
whose father was a neo-nazi
who calls human beings "illegal aliens"
and now is the shadow governor of pete wilson
keepin' hitler's policies alive
while running kkkalifornia

it's not about women

latinos   american indians   blacks
asians   indigenous people

for the last decade
the so-called "civil rights" movement
has been led by ward connerly,   pete wilson
and those like them
who have written pieces of paper
called propositions
trying to control and govern our lives
and then thousands of students
organizers   freedom fighters
get put on the defensive
months later   a proposition passes
and the people lose hope

it's not about saying "no"

we've been saying "no" to
countless propositions & politricks
but

what do we say "yes" to?
what is our alternative?
do we have one?
do we ever?
do we play the game?
choose the lesser of two evils?
do we conform?
give in?
do we play our part?
sing along?
do we get lost in films and entertainment?
or ignore the news?
do we stop reading the papers?
do we give up?
do we become cynical?

or
do we fight?   organize?   mobilize?
do we create our own platform?
our own propositions?
do we build a mass movement?
do we turn on TV and watch it like a hawk?
do we decide not the choose
the lesser of two evils?
do we *"settle for nothing now*
and settle for nothing later?"

for it's not about prop fill-in-the-blank
not about this election
not about tomorrow
but about today and yesterday
see
there's a strangle hold
a crippling amnesia
taking hold of the country
no one cares to ask
why there's a baseball team
called the Texas Rangers™

and why they honor a legacy which lynched more Mexicans
than the klan did blacks

but now the president is part owner
that legacy becomes reality
and the hanging becomes legalized

and why is multiculturalism nothing but a catch phrase
from kinder to 12th grade
as culture becomes
piñatas silly sombreros and spicy food
but it's never about the people

their struggle

their will or their might

see it's not just about prop fill-in-the-blank

it's about our choices

or the lack thereof
our freedom

or the struggle to get it
our justice

so that it's not "just us"
believing that
saying "yes" or saying "no"
is the answer

it's about us sayin' *ya basta'*

organizin' reclaimin' and topplin'

these paper mastas'

and that's when they'll be done enslavin' our people

pos aqui 'estamos listos

gettin' our knowledge from these poems

and reloading our pistols

it's on

and for this empire

there'll be no sequel

. . .

the empire within

i remember hearing stories
of moms being thrown in paddy wagons
for not carrying green cards
and how ins™ agents
raped them as they crossed the border

i was only 5
and they were being *Welcomed to America*™

i remember coming to los angeles
and seeing the difference between
those who have it made
with manicured lawns
on florence avenue
who call cops™ their "PALS"
and those who are assed out on florencia
trying to protect what little they have
with barbed wires
imprisoned windows
and who run from batons
while dodging bullets
from the LAPD™

i remember being taken from los angeles
transplanted to uc berkeley
learning about the Pinay struggle
to kick out the u.s. military
out of the Philippines
and how that parallels
with the struggle in Chiapas
our mom's struggle

the struggle worldwide
but the way i *spoke* began to change

i remember hearing testimonials
from refugees about cia™/fbi™ plots
to create coups all over the world
including Vietnam   Guatemala
and plant drugs on the Panthers in East Oakland
and the Brown Berets in East L.A.

since then i've made a choice to take on empires
with my voice   my life   my heart
and my fist

but as i end my dependence on u.s. history
and u.s. hegemony
i must also battle the empire within

see i've grown to hate liberals
who wear tye-dye shirts
and want to save the whales
but can't see the homeless man
they're stepping on to get to berkeley bowl™
for their organic vegetables

see i've grown
to hate people who hang
dream catchers in their cars
and think all things native are "cute" and hella' deep
but when I speak to them about freeing rocky boice jr.
or leonard peltier
they go deaf from one ear

but that hate is eating me alive
i am becoming prejudice
impatience
shot-calling everything in sight
with little tolerance for another point of view

currently
i am fighting the empire within
fighting this constructed self
that learned to hate the oppressor
while oppressing everyone who didn't think like me

i want to end my dependence on hate
for you can't fight hate with hate
and expect to win

i wanna' be able to take on multi-national corporations
like mcdonald's™
without their coffee breath in my mouth
or nike™
without their swoosh branding everything i wear
as if i
were their cattle

i am fighting the empire within
and if you can't deal with my contradictions
or
if on a scale of perfect revolutionaries
you score a 10
then you probably won't feel me

but if you bump Bob Marley
and not just to get high
but know
that loving thy enemy
is a revolutionary act
and no
that doesn't make me a pacifist
or part of the cool-out squad
    i can still go toe to toe
    but i know
    that we are one world
    one people
    and so

i am fighting

the empire within

and love
as Allah   mi abuelita   Jesucristo
and Marley put it
will indeed reign supreme

and that's my plan of action
for taking on
the empire within

. . .

Things Taken

1 lil, 2 lil, 3 lil indians
get slaughtered
4 lil, 5 lil, 6 lil indians
dead chicken pox
7 lil, 8 lil, 9 lil indians
herded to reservations
and yet
amerikkka celebrates the things taken
land culture language
thingstaken
identity pride
but we'll never give thanks
for pilgrim-led genocide

I will not play the part

you dishonor our people
celebrating columbus day

you lie to our children
with Plymouth Rock™
fairy tales
pretending
pilgrim and "indian" unity
actually existed

1 lil, 2 lil, 3 lil pilgrims

brought on trial

4 lil, 5 lil, 6 lil pilgrims

rounded up deported

7 lil, 8 lil, 9 lil pilgrims

sent to detention camps

for claiming to discover us

for stealing our land

for raping women

for killing us in the name of God

for sharing your diseases

for writing our history

for taking us from our traditions

for forcing us to be like you

for poisoning mother earth

see if then

they *give* thanks

for the

things taken

as justice is served

on our

thanksgiving

. . .

Turning in Your Grave

- A Tribute to César Chávez

i am wearing a
César Chávez t-shirt
driving a car with
César Chávez stickers
on César Chávez Boulevard
passing by
César Chávez School
on César Chávez day
hearing
César Chávez commercials
on the local radio
and seeing
César Chávez billboards
announcing a
César Chávez march
sponsored by multi-national corporations
wondering
if
we praise you
or curse you
when farm-workers are still underpaid
under-appreciated
when immigrants
are scapegoated
when nothing you stood for
is respected

are you being praised
or institutionalized?

are you getting your due?
or being silenced
into a catch phrase?
porque

'Si se puede'

'olvidar la opresión'

'Si se puede'

'convertirte'

into an icon
and forget that
your ideas were never followed
and still aren't today

so i assume you'd rather me not
wear a César Chávez shirt
on César Chávez Boulevard
as i pass by
César Chávez School
on César Chávez Day

but rather
honor you with
justice

fair-wages
equality

and not just trophies
street names and
crumbs

perdónanos César
i hope you'll soon stop turning

in your grave

. . .

<u>veinti-dos fantasmas en elle seretoh</u>

(an ode to the land and people that dwelled in el cerrito,ca.)

the **Ohlone**

head **del norte™**

to see their ancestors

sold en **la plaza™**

by **white knights™**

as **BART™**

& railroads

divide communities and **nations™**

24-hours-a-day

is spanish

a **target™**

at the

ol'west gun room™

cuz

el cerrito™

is never pronounced

as such

except when

governor vicente

and **don peralta**

reigned supreme

but now their land is six feet under

wells fargo™ ATMs

and where

indigenous mexicas dwelled

now they're simply

collectibles™

worth less than **ron's coins™**

time and amnesia

allows descendants

to call land their own

on **eureka™** & **el dorado™**

while poor **san pablo™**

stands in endless lines

at **dmv™**

hoping to ride wild horses

but around here

that's more foreign

that **pier 1 imports™**

so he strolls

to the **blue moon saloon™**

trying to find

saint john the baptist™

to remind the children

that although ghosts

are invisible

they're still around us

and no matter how powerful

are our blinders

they cannot hide

or disguise the truth

welcome to ***elle seretoh***™

come back & visit us

real soon *ya' hear!*

. . .

hollywood™ spell

we are under

a spell

we chuckle

to escape

enter *tame* ment

con tain ment

humanity trapped

like puppets and clowns

as our smiles

are but apathetic enslaved frowns

temporary happiness

continual denial

two hours in a spell of darkness

'clueless**™**'

at times dumb**™**

at others dumber**™**

but always lost or simply spellbound**™**

we are under a spell

continually bound

yet we laugh it off

and pay for it

not just now

but also the next time around

the next time

around

. . .

my philosophy of education

there's no branding
or lining kids up
(in single file lines)

there's no Mr. Cruz
        just césar

no memorizing the 38th president
merely asking kids
to observe 38th Avenue

i ask questions
make students
feel comfortably
uncomfortable

i start with me
where am i
from
opening my own wounds
        most with little
        to no prodding

the stab wound from my father
        leaving 38 stitches
mother called a *puta*
        for having me at age 16
the drugs   the escape
        of a 14-year-old going on 40
knowing these numbers
like punk-ass Pythagoras knew theorems

feeling as if no one understands

but if i want them to open up
i take that first step

i throw up my 'schooling'
when teachers would scar with
words
disdain
sympathy
& charity
and yet
somehow forgetting to
challenge me

i challenge them
to look inward
asking them to define
& redefine self

not just as singular
            but to include family

to consider that the 'downest'
gangster or homegirl on the block
may be grandma

so it's time to clic' up
            find your '*pandilla*'
and bridge communication

as 'assignments'
i have generations
speak to each other
forget cultural vacuums
tonight we're talking
the teenager is interviewing grandpa
and hearing about a new take on the past

i can do this with any subject
in any language

it's simply about humanizing
community building
and empowering
and it's about time

. . .

the terrorist

you can
call me a colombian terrorist
by all means
if it means
that i oppose the lies you spew on TV

Farabundo and Sandino must smile
cuz' they've been taking on
your shady style for
more than a minute

you can plan a coup
and name it operation
u.s.-is-tryin'-to-screw
but i will still stand against you
cuz
we are no longer
blind deaf and dumb
believing the yadi-yada
of the star spangled banner
that disguises
conquest as progress

and if i must pull
a citizen's arrest on george bush
both junior and senior
for the war crimes against
colombianos iraqis
afghanis and centro-americanos
well then
you have the right to remain silent
and everything you say
is currently being used against you
so
you can hire
channels 2, 4, 7 and 11
and pay off
the n.y. and l.a. times
but it is in the people's rhymes
that count 1 of
extortion is filed
against you
for illegally taking power
when your little brother
rigged an election

down there
where the southern heat makes
punching holes in ballots
a task too large for the
average american

and we file count 2
for murder at an unprecedented rate
of Blacks and Latinos on death row
as you served as governor
in hang 'em texas
but had your wardens
do the dirty work
as you stole
both oil & hope
from people who believed
your compassionate conservative
bull

and we file count 3
naming you the world's public enemy
with your lies and fancy media alibis
we know that under the veil
you are the terrorist
in disguise
that we despise

and so I stand
call me a colombian terrorist
label me
pigeonhole me
try and silence me
but I will come at you
with rhymes

protests

and chants

from all directions
til', like Rome,
your empire
crumbles

. . .

***santa fé* riding the Santa Fe**

railroad(ed) faith

grandma smiled and whispered,
"hay que tener fé... nuestra santa fé nos salvará..."

'choo-choo'
derail,
toxic 'progress' we inhale,
as the santa fe train
blazes past our peoples' trail

the catholic priest
asked me to not be afraid
"hay que tener santa fé,"
as he touched me,
and not spiritually,
at age six.

our human god,
steps forth in the Papa-mobile,
  as billions tune in on TV,
his words fill the screens, while silencing the screams,
  with hope
alls while Mexica temples crumble
making room for cathedral number fill-in-the-blank
thanks to the *santa fé* of pope john paul
and those who stand idly by.

on our way to talpa,
the holy land of our goddess,
a man crawled on his knees,

two hundred miles

with *espinas* (thorns),

turned christian crown(s),

on his head

as blood trickled from his veins

he smiled,

my grandpa said,

'el tiene la santa fé...'

a smile,

and tecumseh,

on route 66,

dropped a Molotov cocktail

on the choo-choo

named santa fe

for you the nonbeliever

hay que tener santa fé

. . .

<u>berkeley's™ promises</u>

berkeley™ claims **top dog™** status
espousing ***love not war***™
but **homeless™** prophets must
seek shelter under trees at **"people's" park™**
keeping **(shattuck) down low™**
from **berkeley p.d. raids™**
cuz **blondie™**(s) and brunette
cops beat down resistance
behind not just the **asian ghetto™**
while this year's fresh fish dream of revolution
sprouting like **amoebas™**
but **campanille's™** bell
awaken today's **urban outfitter™ hippies™**
that in the **reel™** world
the **free speech movement™**
is merely a café

you can **telegraph™**
what u say on **sproul hall™**
but ur competing with multiple voices
as you send echoes into the **bear's lair™**
where **freedom fighters™**
are a **haas™** been
cuz now those who decide
how berkeley can you be™
dwell in city hall
and even **oski™** thinks
they're clowning around

as- u- c™

and u say diversity

we see **the gap™**

between your fancy brochures

and drop out rates

of black & brown faces

left merely as traces

in **copwatch™** videos

of the victim the popo is chasin'

and no we don't

need corner **fortune tellers™**

or ol' **rasputin™**

pushin' **revolution books™**

while kickin'

the aforementioned

homeless prophet out da' store

for not affording

bob avakian's manifesto™

nor do we need vegan gurus

selling us overpriced fruits

at **berkeley bowl™**

claiming nothing but health

at **chez panisse™**

but can't give the undocumented worker

who prepared that salad

a living wage

berkeley™

spare us your promises

clothed in

third world **tye-dye™** t-shirts
that can't seem to cover
anything you claim to stand for
as
self-proclaimed
vanguard™ leaders
drop tired clichés
of **revolution™**
while sipping $4 lattes
at **café strada™**
but can't seem
to make the 15 minute **BART™** ride
to richmond
to put their theory into action

you can claim the **left™**
making you actually **right™**
about convincing
wide-eyed 18-year-olds
much like the military
that you are the way   the **answer™** (**coalition**)
when in fact you're developing a cancer
that not even the **berkeley free clinic™**
can take out.

.   .   .

y también apesta tu mierda

this is a love poem, cuz I wouldn't check u if I didn't love u

dear brother from another mother
so you approach me with long hair
stare at my military cut and judge what's new

you speak of *indigenismo*
and the sixth sun (son)
but you can't even take care of your 5th
4th or 3rd one

don't pimp *indigenismo*
to hate in 4 directions
while cheating (& lying) on 3 women
choosing to live 2 lives
when all you really need is 1 mirror

like you my shits stinks too
but when i talk to you
you seem more interested
in keepin' your timbalands™ clean
and i see your eyes stroll by
as that lady passes you by
you could care less about what i have to say
but merely about gettin' high

and no you don't need to flex
showing off your che™ tatted-up pecks
pretending to be hard
so you don't get jumped on the boulevard
or when you spit to her trying to *act* revolutionary

quoting marx™, lenin™ and mao™
tired dead men
man don't you see
your shits' dead tired

and you my sister from another mister
you righteous now ok
it ain't my biz to say just yesterday
you were from around the way
but ok change is possible
on any given day

it's great you taking womyn studies classes
but don't pimp feminism
when you backstabbing *tú hermana*
when she's not around
ayer hoy y mañana

you tell me you a man hater now
and you can't stand my kind
ok if that's going to free you
then take it out on me today
but don't forget
you can't fight hate with hate and expect to win
see my shit like your shit stinks too
and when i try to approach you
about lolita, haydeé, lucy and assata
you say "who"
"I'm just trying to get up in the club too"
what?
that's just fakin' the funk stay true

maybe

when brother-man gets through with the mirror

he can pass it over to you

so you can wipe off the glitter

that like you is fake and phony too

and won't stay on even with elmer's™ glue

shot callers   be critical of me

i got skeletons in the closet

that are way past rottin'

but don't forget

that for every finger pointed at me

there's about four-five pointed straight at you

before you claim

to know and speak the truth

don't forget to wipe your ass

and know that your shit stinks too

.   .   .

faith and i: what do i say yes to?

publicly i've been saying no to war
187/209/227 and countless
other propositions
we've been saying no to racism,
sexism, homophobia
        but what do i say yes to?
        what do i believe in?
        what do i have faith in?

privately   do i say yes to my stepfather
who holds out his hand apologizing
for another verbal assault
with budweiser™ on his breath

do i say yes to mom when she says
        "mijo can i have a vacation after 20 years,
        i just wanna go to méxico
        but not for a funeral"
and i bust a fake smile
while checkin' my empty pockets
knowin' we can't afford it
and she'll never get the days off

how can i not say yes
to grandma & her alzheimer's
        when she asks me if these pills
will let her keep her memory
for at least one more year
even if i know it's a lie
and those little white pills can't slow down   time

how can i tell my students

        "yes, war will end soon"

        "they'll let your daddy out of prison"

"don't worry that they just built prison #23

        but they still can't finish another UC,™

        you *do* have a future"

and do so with a straight face

i wanna say yes to hope i do   i do

i wanna hold hope in my arms or have hope hold me

i wanna have answers   and still empower you

or at least empower me

i wanna grow towards God

but i'm slippin' and not just into darkness

but insanity

my actions say yes to denial

i try to deal with it

by making sarcasm my friend

and now

i find myself trusting nothing and no-one

and yet

i need to say yes   to faith

but i fear   faith and i

are having marital problems

and she wants a divorce

faith, will you please

just say yes to me?

. . .

¡Qué en paz descanse!

Don Angel Villafaña- mi abuelito

Poemas en Español

mi propia canción

"La migra a mi me agarró
300 veces digamos
pero jamás me domó
a mi me hizo los mandados"

la migra a mi me agarró
pero esa primera vez
sentí casi 300 macanazos
en frente de mi amada
me humillaron
que si era 'wetback' me preguntaron
y pues a la cárcel me llevaron

"Yo se bién que estoy afuera
pero el día que yo me muera
se que tendrás que llorar
llorar y llorar"

yo se bién que estoy afuera
ahí el policía sonríe
porque su bala sangra mi pecho
y en este día que yo muero
nadie sale a llorar
a llorar y a llorar

"Lastima que seas ajena
y no tengo llave para abrir tu cuerpo…
lastima que seas ajena
el fruto prohibido que jamás comí…"

lastima que sos ajena
no eres dueña de tu propio cuerpo
de solo 15 años
y ya esclava a tu propio padre
que te considera una fruta
que diario come

"Señora no lo quite años a su vida
póngale vida a los años que es mejor"
señora quien le quitó los años a su vida
y si los tuviera póngale valor a su mente
no tiene que ser objeto sexual
pa' ninguna canción
que pretende ser conciente
"Dicen que soy un desastre total
que soy mala hierba"
mi consejero me aconsejó
que soy un desastre total
una mala hierba
por no haberme tatuado
el tricolor norteamericano
que me convierte en propiedad
de los estamos jodidos

y así fue
que la migra me agarro
afuera llorando
como propiedad ajena
envejeciendo
dañándome mi espíritu
llamándome mala hierba
y por eso es que ahora
ya no prendo el radio
y busco poder cantar
mi propia canción

. . .

nuestra marcha

Latinos, Indígenas, Mestizos
con raíces por todo el continente
cargamos tristeza, lágrimas y sacrificio
hemos llegado
unidos
sin ser vencidos
al punto clave de nuestra historia

unos agotados
cansados
otros heridos   por la multitud de golpes sociales
queriéndonos aplastar

en nuestros barrios han sido
empujadas las drogas por departamentos
policíacos que buscan neutralizar
nuestra existencia

en nuestras calles tenemos menos
libros y mas pistolas
para destruirnos los unos a los otros

en nuestras escuelas nos enseñan
que fuimos indios salvajes
conquistados por Cortéz y Colón
negándonos nuestra cultura
nuestra propia historia
nuestra existencia

nuestros gobiernos prefieren
estafar a nuestros pueblos
con corrupción, guerra y muerte
como tácticas de represión

los ricos oprimen y abusan a los pobres
los hombres han querido adueñarse
y buscan conquistar a las mujeres
pero nadie, digo nadie
    ha podido domar
     a nuestro espiritú
     a nuestra llama
     a nuestro fuego
     a nuestra humildad
     a nuestra lucha
    y a nuestro corazón

en la hora de nuestra unión
con cicatrices de abuso
de violaciones a nuestros derechos humanos
con la pus de sangre podrida
de macanazos, balazos,
y abusos sexuales
tenemos que levantar el alma
hacia el firmamento
con fé que este pueblo
y esta lucha
es de nosotros
para nosotros
y por nosotros

. . .

la revolución personal

una soledad profunda
eterna
el pensar que mi lucha
tú lucha
nuestra lucha
ha llegado ha un final

cada vez que uno se levanta a enfrentar
sus hipocresías
a cambiar su condición social
ahí hay otra persona que lo traiga hacia abajo

pensamientos adoloridos
del aquel que traicionó
con aquella voz o palabra
que dañó tú imagen propia
de un gran héroe

existes solamente en tu propia mentira

atraes moscas hambrientas
y al verte en el espejo
ves las lágrimas correr
por tu piel
las que ya no quieres sentir

eso mi compañera
es el principio de la revolución
personal

. . .

a quién le importe

para las mujeres que luchan en juárez, en méxico, mundial

me culpas porque busco

comida

espacio pa' vivir

un día libre

mi voz

me culpas

porque trabajo en la calle

porque vendo mi cuerpo para comprar agua

que aquí apesta más que tus palabras

pa' darle un baño a mi bebé

me culpas

porque trabajo en la fábrica *accel*™ y nunca estoy en casa

pero ya me dieron más horas

entro a las 6 salgo a las 6

y este año solo he tenido que ir a la clínica 6 veces

ya ni siento mis manos

haciendo ropa pa' '*tropical sportswear*™

y se qué se la llevan a quentáqui (kentucky) por juárez

me vale que no tengo pa' comprar esa ropa

alcabo esta re' fea

pinchis güeras yo no se como se ponen esa porquería

y no me hables de lo que me pongo

alcabo no me vas a comprar nada, sabes,

lencha vio la compañía en el norte pero ayá se llama *elamex*™

como son bien mameis los patrones

y no me culpes

por no ir a misa

es mi único día de descanso ¡y sí voy a dormir!

que crees que me voy a levantar a las 6 pa' hacerte de almorzar

'tas loco vete a trabajar mendigo

y ya te vi con mi hija no te pases de listo
ponle una mano y te lo juro que te mato
no me culpes
porque no fui a sepultar a mi prima
si me hubiera salido del trabajo me hubieran corrido
y tú quien eres pa' juzgarme
tú ni siquiera le hablaste a los judiciales pa' que cubrieran su cuerpo
y los reporteros en mi cara preguntándome que si tengo miedo
de salir a la calle
me hacen los mandados
les dije que se vayan a la fregada
no te creas
pos' que les voy a decir
la policía no hace nada
los judiciales bien pendejos
el gobierno de aquí y de allá quieren puras mordidas
el patrón solo te quiere cuando andas bien
nomás te enfermas y te corre
a ellos les vale madre
a los norteños puro interés
a los gabachos solo quieren su ropa en especial
a los pochos se hacen mensos que
según ellos
ya son ciudadanos
no manches nopaleros
y nomás hay pedo
y la migra los corre de texas
sí, le dije al reportero, hay un chingo de cosas mal aquí
por donde quieres que empiece
y al reportero le valió
y se fue a cubrir otro funeral

. . .

chavalo de la ciudad

para el pandillero y la chola...

chavalo de la ciudad
atrapado
títere al patrón del tick-tock
        marca rolex™
pero solamente plateado
que controla tus minutos cada día

la ciudad
        te sonríe
pero toda chueca
y te promete sueños
que sin saber
se convierten en pesadillas

es viernes por la tarde
sales a la calle
disfrazado
        atraes miedo
pero en realidad
        ¿quien te pela?
        ¿quien te ve?
        ¿a quien le importas?

chavalo de la ciudad
encadenado
        en un coma moral
esclavizado

y eres apenas un chavo
pero dices
"pues me escapo
en el mentado 'trago'"

claro
no es nada raro
el chavo ha sido agarrado del rabo
por la trampa
            sin escape
de un barrio creado
aquí
en *los estamos jodidos*
donde nos quieren
"a sus ordenes" diario
matándonos por pendejadas
y atacándonos
utilizando el
azul y *colorado* de su bandera
que nos hemos puesto
según
convirtiéndonos
en norteños y sureños
dividiéndonos
pa' que el *blanco*
se quede con los dos lados
de nuestra tierra

enfrentamos una lucha
personal   social

en trampa total
en cual
hemos empeñado hasta nuestro nopal
que crece sangriento
de esto no miento
pero si quieres
olvida mi estupidez
que vuela en el viento
que ya ni siquiera sientes
por ser
el mas *'cool'*
de los *'cool-leros'*

pero no te agüites
al cabo las cajas de muerto
hasta las encuentras
a dos por uno
porque no piensan
que valemos nada
en este mundo

pero si piensas lo contrario
¿pues que esperas?
'Ya es tarde.'
y pa' cambiar tú rabia
en acción
queda poco tiempo.
. . .

¡No llores Ché Guevara!

•un tributo a nuestro comandante

Dicen que la distancia es el olvido,
¿Pero será que te recuerdo,
en un mundo donde las palabras
y los hechos muy rara vez se encuentran,
y cuando se encuentran no se saludan,
porque no se reconocen?

¿Será porque viajaste de isla
a campo por todo Latino-América
buscando una mano,
y recibiste casi siempre una cachetada?

¿Será porque fuiste al rescate
de compatriotas Africanos
cuando tus mismos compañeros
se reían llamándole a tus hechos una estupidez?

¿Será porque lloraste hincado,
solo y agotado,
cuando otros te pisoteaban
por recibir la porquería de gloria
que se te brindaba?

No puede ser que por tus lágrimas lloro,
que por tu pluma escribo,
que por tu pulmón respiro,
y por tu corazón vivo.

¿Será que por ti vivimos
con el sueño y la pesadilla de la libertad?

¿Será?

¿Será tu voz la que gritó
Tupac Amarú,
y la escuchamos como terrorismo,
sin entender su misión?

Tantas preguntas,
y tan pocas respuestas...

Pero ni te preocupes,
por si será cierto que la distancia es el olvido,
no tienes nada de que preocuparte,
desde en cuando
que nuestro mundo tenga
hambre,
sed,
y deseo de libertad,
estarás lo más cerca de nuestro pecho,
de nuestra alma,
y de nuestro corazón...

compatriota ya no llores,
¡acuérdate, qué nunca nos vencerán!

. . .

Malcolm X

Black & White Drawing by **Jazmin Preciado-Cruz**

Commentaries

César A. Preciado-Cruz pays his respects at the gravesite of Malcolm X

Hartsdale, New York

Thizz, Grills, 'The Town' (Oakland), Malcolm X and da' Youth

Can or should a Mexican even speak on Black Liberation? This is not even about that. Malcolm X is my shining prince. He is a living example of how I can transform my life and stand up for freedom by any means necessary.

As I have been observing "The Town," Oakland, CA., and I have also checked out East L.A., having grown up there, the east side of Chicago and the east side of New York, something strange is happening all over again.

We are being led to go dumb! Corporate Hiphop music, which is the one played on the radio and TV stations such as MTV™, BET™ teach us the following:

1. **Do/Pop Pills**. Mac Dre popularized the THIZZ movement as another way of glamorizing the feeling that you get when you are high from various types of pills. These pills come to "The Town" from the invisible South Oakland. South Oakland is the non-existent place where boats are docked that come from many places including Puerto Rico and Colombia. These boats arrive from places like Puerto Rico where the island was taken over (occupied) by pharmaceutical (drug) companies in the 1940s/50s with Operation Bootstrap. Black and Brown people need to be kept 'high' so they never realize who is jacking them up. That's why we need rappers like Mac Dre to make putting poison in your body popular. That's where Mac Dre, Keak da Sneak and others come along.

Malcolm X, then Malcolm Little, then Detroit Red connects big time because he did all kinds of drugs, as many of our youth are doing today.

2. **Smoke Purple/Reefers**: Getting and staying high is crucial in order to keep people not ever really thinking about anything but getting rid of the pain of daily living. During Malcolm's time *'smoking purple'* meant smoking reefers. Youth are never told that hitting one joint is like smoking 20 cigarettes to the lungs. Or they are never told about the brain cells that get lost. Why tell them, let 'em think it's cool. Why not even have them sing songs about it all the time.

3. **Shooting Dice/Runnin' Numbers**: Since jobs are hard to come by for teens, and resorting to selling weed or cocaine becomes a bit dangerous, many youth resort to making some pocket money by gambling. It is a welcomed addiction with entire cities created like Las Vegas, Reno and Atlantic City. During Malcolm's time, he would run numbers and now the youth shoot dice, play poker or bones to make some ends. America tells us that 'we gotta' have money. Money somehow becomes the most important thing to have.

4. **<u>Looking Sharp/Buying Material 'Crap'</u>**: During Malcolm's time he had to look sharp with his zoot suits, and now the youth are constantly sold products left and right. The youth are even sold shoes by making 3-minute commercials that actually seem like songs such as the catchy jingle "got my vans on, but they look like sneakers."

5. **<u>The Need to 'Floss' (Grills)</u>**: Showing off what we don't have is not a new phenomenon. But our 'going dumb' culture has reached an all-time high as somehow we have convinced the youth that it is cool to wear metal in your mouth. The new 'grills' movement led by Nelly, Paul Wall and other hired goons, is about helping young people poison themselves quickly. Imagine having the ability to make youth pay $200-500 to put metal in their mouths as it seeps into their saliva and the residue poisons their body.

6. **<u>Need to make drinking 'the thing' to do</u>**: In East Oakland, East L.A., the east sides of Chicago and New York, there are liquor stores on every corner. Young Malcolm believed he loved to drink. It is no coincidence that on every corner the government gives liquor licenses so easily to businesses to keep the youth drunk. When people drink they develop so-called beer muscles and that's when fights break out. Also, you find malt liquor in the form of 40 ouncers in the hood, to 'jack up' the youth quicker. Companies like St. Ides**™** caught on quick that the best way to make drinking popular is to use rappers like Ice Cube, Notorious B.I.G., Tupac and so many others to sell their poison. It's working! Just ask Lil' Jon, he'll tell you, *"I drink [Seagram's Gin™] and they payin' me for it!"*

So what does all this have to do with Malcolm, 'The Town' we rep', and even the youth? Malcolm was also being sold all of this:

1. pills
2. weed
3. gambling
4. clothes/material goods
5. need to floss (make money)
6. alcohol

So how did he escape? Why should someone from 'The Town' care about Malcolm?

Malcolm was also told that he wasn't worth anything.

1. **<u>Going Dumb (Let's not get an education) and Proud of It:</u>**

What if the government could hire actors (pseudo rappers) and have them create a 'yellow bus,' 'going retarded,' 'dumb,' culture where knowledge would be the kryptonite (only thing that could stop Superman**™**) for Black and Brown youth. Malcolm faced that. It wasn't until he arrived in prison that he realized all this time that he had been in prison. In prison he realized he was 'hella dumb,' and not proud of it. So, while in prison, he read the entire dictionary and couldn't stop reading his story, history. In prison, he learned that the government was setting him up to be a slave.

Our youth are being set up to be slaves. So what can we learn from Malcolm? Even if I come from:

1. **a broken home**: Malcolm's mom was considered crazy, his dad was killed, and all his brothers/sisters were separated and put in foster homes.

2. **a world where cash and prostitution rule my life**: Malcolm, as a teenager, considered himself a pimp and had little to no respect for women.

3. **a world filled with violence.**

Malcolm transformed himself. Here's how:

1. began to understand that he had been lied to.

2. stopped believing in the cash/drugs/guns set-up that the government had for him.

3. began to study for freedom.

-read entire dictionary to learn the meaning of all words.

-read about his roots, Africa, the motherland to be grounded.

-read about his people's struggles.

-connected to the Most High, in his case Allah, and began to realize that his body is a temple and not a trash can to dump any kind of 'crap' in.

-stopped wanting drugs because he knew they were government poison. No more alcohol, pills or weed.

-stopped cursing because he wanted to be able to 'tell someone off' without needing to curse.

-stopped trying to be White by no longer bleaching (conking) his hair. Became proud of his hair, proud of what he looked like.

-realized that he is a king.

-realized that he is a warrior, and began walking like one.

So why should we care about Malcolm X?

Because Malcolm provides a powerful example that anyone can change.

No matter how 'messed up' things are in the 'hood, we can change.

Malcolm also found his voice. He stopped being shy or afraid to speak out. Once he knew the truth, no one could shut him up. Too many of our youth are embarrassed to even go up in front of the class to speak.

Your silence will not protect you.

It is time to honor Malcolm.   It is time to honor yourself.

I refuse to be a slave to pills, alcohol and the ghetto the government has created for me.

I am no-one's prostitute.

I am somebody.   I am strong. I am proud.

That is the gift that Malcolm has left us.

The gift is that we no longer need to be slaves.

It is time to open it.

...

W.A.S.H. M.E. of American History

As Americans, we are taught a history as winners, victors, manifestly destined rulers of the free world.

As Americans, we've entered every part of the 'civilized or so-called uncivilized' world. Flashbacks of Panamá, Bosnia, Angola and Taiwan.

As Americans, we've stolen the lands inhabited by Indigenous People and claim them to be our own. Yet we so arrogantly ignore this as ancient history. Flashbacks of the Philippines, Puerto Rico, Hawaii, and Turtle Island (Anahuak, now known as the United States.)

As Americans, we've taken coolies, slaves, debt-peons from their lands and brought them over in chains to plow, rake, and build our empire.

As Americans, we salute, honor, and claim as our ultimate rights those hailing from the constitution.

A constitution created by Anglo-Saxon, elite, heterosexual, racist, sexist, classist men who owned slaves but spoke of freedom.

We as Americans, proudly salute the American flag and are willing to go to great lengths to defend it.

We as Americans, would justify, rape, murder, mass destruction, and even dropping an atom bomb for the sake of retaining our power. Flashbacks of Hiroshima and Nagasaki.

We as Americans, would lie, distort the truth, and teach young people a false imperialistic history of conquest shadowing it with notions of democracy.

We as Americans, have set up military bases in other people's countries, to protect them, from them.

We as Americans, control the global economy and can regulate the worth, the prices of goods, minerals, food, and of human beings based on our need.

We as Americans, control the norms, behaviors, actions, myths, legends, and tales of the world by invading it with our antennas, television sets, VCR's, films and our beliefs.

We as Americans, fear change.

We as Americans, can not hear the complete other side. We only know our side.

We as Americans, are right. That is, if we were to ever be wrong, we would repress, seek and destroy what we fear the most: our ignorance of the world.

We as Americans, are hypocrites.

We as Americans, are our own worst enemy. We are our turmoil.

Who are we, as Americans? Historically, politically, economically, socially, we are: ONE. The rest of us have screamed: "WASH ME, WASH ME, for the closer I am to YOU, the closer I am to being an American."

We are **W**hite, **A**nglo-**S**axon, **H**eterosexual, **M**ale **E**lites.

So who are the illegal aliens, who are the indigenous people?

Who are the creatures from the other world?

Women. People characterized as having 'color.'

The poor. Those with distinct characteristics: darker skin, stretched out eyes, foreign tongues, 'back-ward' cultures, and vaginas.

The 'crooked': the lesbian, gay, bisexual and trans-gender. Deviants. Freaks.

What can we, as Americans do? We as Americans, can, should, and must continue to imprison physically by building more jails.

Economically, by chewing and spitting out more workers, at the cheapest of wages, for the growth of our world-wide corporations. In education, by teaching a false patriotic history blinding the masses of youth today.

But, if they escape or revolt what must we as Americans do?

Deport, prosecute, scapegoat and kill all indigenous & illegal aliens.

What do we, the non-americans, the third world people, women, the aged, the poor, the 'colored,' the different, the foreign-tongued and the deviant do?

We as people of the world can, should, and must ask ourselves the following:

Do we not have the right to enforce the sanctity of our humanity by any means necessary?! Then that time has come, brace yourself.

. . .

‘Chapetes’ & ‘Scraps’: Raza Blasting Raza As Our Slavery Continues

Norteños & Sureños Fight While We Bury Our Future

Rest-In-Peace t-shirt companies, funeral homes, casket warehouses, coroner’s offices, prisons and many governments are making a ‘killing’ off of Raza blasting Raza.

Since the end of the **Mexican-American War** in 1848 we have been divided as the U.S. stole 1/3 of México’s land and we became either ***Pochos*** or ***Mojados*** all because of a border. Now we kill and die for the red and the blue. It is no coincidence that both colors appear in the U.S. flag, as it represents the place where we shed blood for barrios that we do not own.

Not only do we not know why we fight, but we don’t even know who our real heroes are. Hollywood has made it its sole purpose to give us fake heroes such as **Scarface.™** Did you know that **Scarface™** is played by an Italian, Al Pacino, pretending to be Cuban with a fake Spanish-accent ‘straight-clowning’ our language and our people? But we bought it. We buy it at every swap meet, flea market and now even all over America’s malls. We fell for their trap. We are not taught that we had heroes from the north and the south who united and ‘banged’ for the people. **Pancho Villa** was from the north and proud of it, while **Emiliano Zapata** was from the south. They met in México’s capital and when they united they posed a serious threat to the Mexican government because they were fighting to give land to the poor and not the rich.

Did you know that in California we are becoming the majority? But did you also know that in South Africa ‘Black’ Africans are the majority, but it is ‘White’ Africans that are in power? How did that happen? --‘Black’ Africans were taught to hate themselves and to kill each other. They call that system ‘**apartheid**.’ It is straight legal slavery.

Check this out: In California we have Raza from all over, but instead of uniting we split ourselves up into **Norteños, Sureños, Mara Salvatrucha, Mexican Mafia, Nuestra Familia, Paisas, Latin Kings/Queens, Border Brothers/Sisters** and so many more cliques.

In schools do they really teach us our history? Do you know much about **Lolita Lebrón** (Puerto Rico), **Haydeé Santamaría** (Cuba), **Elvia Alvarado** (Honduras), **Lucy González-Parsons** (Mexican-American), **Valentina Ramírez** (México), **César Sandino** (Nicaragua), or **Farabundo Martí** (El Salvador)? They don’t teach us about heroes and sheroes because these are some real OGs who ‘banged’ for freedom. Nowadays if they teach us anything about our history the answer to everything is ‘**César Chávez**.’ That’s all they want us to know. But some of our youth do not even know that ‘Chávez’ was from the North, a **Norteño,** who believed in ‘non-violence.’ So it makes no sense why Norteños would throw up the UFW red flag as their own and straight blast on Paisas or Sureños. Would Chávez do that? It's like we are spitting on his grave.

But it's hard out on the streets. Depending on what color you wear, what flag you claim, it may mean your life. But why do you think that is?

When a Mexican wearing blue kills a Chicano wearing red do you think that helps our people somehow? This 'pleito' (fight) dates back to 1848. To the U.S. government we are all 'beaners' and 'wetbacks.' They don't care if you change your name from María to Mary or call yourself a 'U.S.' Citizen, you are still as Carlos Mencia states, "Nothing but **U.B.S.** (United Beaner Service) what can Brown do for you?" All we do is serve others, but when do we serve ourselves?

I know homies who claim Florencia in Los Angeles, La Villita in Chicago, and 38th Street in Oakland, but do we own any of these blocks? We die daily for these streets, but these streets could care less about us.

Raza, I'm not asking you to stop gang-banging. The choice is yours. But if you are going to 'bang,' why not 'bang' for freedom? Did you know that there have been many OGs who have been 'gang-banging' for freedom since day one?

We can take it 19th-century-old-school style with OGs like **Tiburcio Vasquez, Gregorio Cortez** and **Joaquin Murrieta**. The U.S. government called them bandits, we call them heroes. They had 'clicas' riding for freedom and to reclaim the land.

In the 20th century we had OGs like **Valentina Ramírez** who disguised herself as a man in order to be able to fight during the Mexican Revolution. Then there are Puerto Rican and Cuban OGs, like **Lolita Lebron** and **Haydeé Santamaría**, who in the 1950s 'banged' for freedom. Lolita stormed into the U.S. House of Representatives on July, 1954 and demanded that Puerto Rico be free. Haydeé was one of the real sheroes of the Cuban revolution back when **Ché Guevara** was still riding around like a rich kid in his motorcycle.

Then we had some ex-gangsters who started groups like the **Young Lords** in Chicago and New York, and the **Brown Berets** in East L.A. These sisters and brothers defended our people against the police and fought for us to have our own hospitals, schools, and our own spots like Chicano Park in San Diego.

Today, in any barrio you go to we don't own our own streets. We aren't the ones going to college because we hate schools. "It's hella boring," we say. It's boring on purpose. This government wants us to drop out so that we can commit small crimes and end up in jail. Did you know that they have built 23 new prisons in California and only 1 new university (UC Merced) in the last 20+ years?! Why do you think that is? Under the **13th Amendment** of the

Constitution this country can still have 'slaves' once someone is a prisoner. So it makes sense to build many prisons for Raza in California. We are the new slaves!

Now that we know, I don't think any of us would want to be a slave for the U.S. But if you do, go ahead and shoot, stab, and kill your people. If you want to be a slave go ahead and sell that rock and commit the crimes you need to commit. There are plenty of prisons waiting for you, and that's '*por vida*' (for life).

If they don't get us one way, they try and get us another. In most barrios there are hundreds of spots where we can get liquor; bars, carnicerías, stores, restaurants, and gas stations because the plan is to make sure that poor people are always 'on' something. If poor people are high or buzzed they are more likely to commit crimes and then become U.S. slaves. Did you know that 'poppin' pills is all part of the plan to get us addicted to something?

Wake up Raza! That red or blue rag, that's Made in Taiwan,™ is not what we are about. Our roots don't begin with the colors of the U.S. flag. Our roots go back to Incas, Mayas and Mexicas.

What would happen if you start 'banging' for freedom? What would happen if you didn't steal from your people, but from the rich to give to the poor? What would happen if red or blue weren't your enemies, but your enemies were those who ride in red and blue vehicles that seek to make us slaves? What would happen if we 'got' educated and stood up for ourselves? What would happen if we stopped turning on ourselves, and to ourselves? That's what 'I'm down to ride for!' See you on the avenues as we reclaim the streets!

...

It's not Bombs or War

u.s. sanctions
banning food for babies
to teach adults to bow down
to democrapitalism
causes malnutrition to no-nutrition
leaving corpses in overpriced cemeteries
but no-one calls it bombing or an act of war

water fountains pumping polluted water in
barrio and ghetto school playgrounds
lead to weak stomachs, poisoning children daily
but no-one calls it bombing or war

policy decisions written on laptops
passed by men in suits
send anyone labeled "terrorists"
to concentration camps
to rehabilitate via electric shocks
'til eyeballs pop out
leaving scorched bodies
and silencing dissent
    but it's never called war

teaching white history where
whites did this and whites led that
and whites are mighty & great
creates inferiority complexes
for nonwhite kids
where they hate themselves   hate school
hate his story   hate each other
hate their neighbors

fight their neighbors
eventually kill their neighbors
but it's never called
an act of war

regulating
how many babies
black brown red yellow womyn
can or can't have
by forced sterilization
sticking needles in vaginas
wipes out
the next generation
in the name of over population
but it's never called war

this president
this government
this country claiming to be america
has been murdering children
dumbing down education
locking up opposition
misfeeding the world
on as many levels
as there are hungers
poisoning the water
and destroying womyn
but it is never called war

nor should it be

it's an act of genocide

and that's what we honor

when we honor

this country's dic   tator

this country's   president

it is with much intent

that we destroy everything

except those in power

and that's

what's being inaugurated

every 4 years

and that

in a nutshell

is 'thee american way'

but never to be confused

with bombings

or war

.   .   .

A letter to my son (to be)

Dear baby,

I have wanted to write to you for quite some time now. I have been struggling with how to 'teach you' all that you need to know before society tries to fill you with lies.

On your first birthday I want you to open the gift of 'self-determination.' You probably won't know what that means yet; all in due time.

Your mom and I hope to guide you on the path of freedom, but be patient, because believe it or not, as we speak you are guiding us on that path.

We hope to teach you not to value products or material goods, but to value the beauty in the struggle for justice and equality.

Your first day of school will not be when you turn 5. We are your school.

We hope to surround you with *tíos* and *tías* that will teach you the truth.

Believe it or not many people hate you and your people. We don't share this to make you cry, but to strengthen your resolve.

We will not fill you with hate, but with love. But we will also not blind you.

At 'formal' school, your teacher will probably butcher or exoticize your name.

Your name, Santiago Olin, means "*The Chosen One of the Movement.*"

You were created with lots of love.

On occasion, you will have to *teach* your teachers with love, and lots of patience.

They will mispronounce your name.

The will be surprised that you can already speak at least 2 languages.

They may accredit it to the fact that you have 2 u.c. berkeley alum parents. That is not the case. We come well educated from *madres* who never got colonized in their schools.

No! Tylenol is not the only remedy for pain. *Yerba buena*, *manzanilla* and sage will help you heal.

You will have much to share at "show and tell," but don't show off. Just share.

Explain to them why we smudge people with sage at ceremonies.

When they have you wear fake feathers for "Thanksgiving Day," tell them about the genocide and the resistance.

We will probably be in the principal's office a lot.

Yes! You can refuse to pledge allegiance, but make sure you tell them why. We support you!

You will not see your people much in the 'assigned reading,' but when it's time for book reports hit 'em with Lolita Lebron. More on her later.

Don't make fun of kids wearing glasses, being bigger or smaller, or joke that girls can't play kickball. Think and share your own thoughts, even if you are the only one.

Stand up against injustice, even in the lunch line.

Ok, I don't wish to overwhelm you.

Life will be/is beautiful, even during the hard times.

Never question whether or not your mommy and I love you, we do, unconditionally.

You are a young Mexica(n) warrior, in training, so be on-point, especially when no-one is watching.

Be whatever you want to be but understand that you are here on Earth to give and not take.

Don't be afraid to dream.

I love you.

I can't wait to hold you, but please don't pee on my face too much.

Love,

Tu papa César

. . .

i pray for strength
for my convictions to never waver
for me to stand
and even if i feel that i'm the only one
that i not feel alone
that i always remember
we are many worldwide standing for freedom

i wanna face my own demons
face what i wanna change and do it
without hurting myself
without depression or masochism
apathy or laziness holding me back

i wanna see people not lose hope
i wanna see people holding hands again
or holding hands for the first time
standing with and not against each other
as we fight for freedom
in its many forms
believing we can
change anything including ourselves

i wanna see this movement grow evolve embrace
while dodging chase™ manhattan bank that is
and all corporate puppet masters
including this empire

i wanna us to use our credit cards less or not at all
to learn to grow our own food
to use traditional medicine

and not depend on chemicals for false healing

i want us to reconnect with our spirit
be it mother earth, tonantzin,
jahweh, jesus, buddha, allah,
the great spirit, the most high
the creator or nameless

i want us to believe in ourselves
and our ability to change
grow dream & create
as we learn to love ourselves
and not need someone else to give us
self-worth

i wanna open these kinds of gifts on christmas
and have these types of resolutions
for the coming year
for my coming lifetime

but more than anything
i wanna make them
my living philosophy
who i am
not who i want to be

creator
i pray for all who are suffering from multiple hungers
be it for food
for change for salvation
for hope for faith
for breath for another day

for the desire to live
for the ability to face the mirror
to face self
to face so called enemies
to face another version of self
and change

these are actually inexpensive
and priceless gifts
that i can give myself and the world
for as i change self
I change the world
and those i touch
those i reach

help me creator to help myself
to heal myself
to strengthen myself
to prepare for the coming battles
the coming arrows
the coming attacks
the haters   or rather   the not yet innovators

open my eyes   their eyes   our eyes
so we can see
self   others   as one
as not separate but equal   as connected
as one
that's all i want
for christ's mass
and the coming new year.

. . .

If I could be like spook

like *spook* i too *sat by the door*
pretendin' from da' start
that i'm wit' ya (mr. colony)

never did they know
that we're preparin' to go toe-to-toe
and if you plan to stop us with
'Inner City Riot Control'
good luck
this 'underground guerrilla army'
is ready fearless
will die for freedom
lives for freedom
with love as our anthem

no need for hate & oppression
to win our liberation
but we will bust a cap to escape this plantation

your days are numbered
you can kill the head
kill me or any one member
but this is no snake
it's a movement
a circle a people
determined not just 2 be equal
cuz' it's reparations time
and we're here to collect our due.

. . .

thank yous

Thank you Immortal Technique for speaking out.

Thank you Yuri Kochiyama for never giving up.

Thank you Mumia for not letting time do you.

Thank you Tijerina for taking back the land
or at least trying to.

Thank you Lolita Lebron for storming the
u.s. house of representatives. *You bad!*

Thank you Malcolm X for spittin' truth to power.

Thank you Haydeé Santamaría for fighting
with your heart. Sorry we let you down.

Thank you Lucy Gonzalez for speaking out even
when they banned you from Chicago.

Thank you American Indian Movement
for taking on the c.i.a.

Thank you Black Panthers
for taking on the police and self-hatred.

Thank you Young Lords for taking over the hospital
and letting your roots just flow.

Thank you Brown Berets for walking out of school
and trying to walk into knowledge.

Thank you Audre Lorde for not speaking with silence.

Thank you Abuelita for not giving up on life.

Thank you Abuelito for always nurturing seeds.
We still growin'.
The crop may not seem that great, but there's still time.

Thank you Mama for not aborting,
for putting my body on your back.

Thank you my partner for teaching me
that love is not a noun.

Thank you!
Thank you ALL!
Thank you!

. . .

East Oakland Youth with

Nane Alejandrez

Founder-Barrios Unidos

N Sur Gentes with

Elaine Brown

Black Panther

Angela Davis

Black Panther, Professor

Reies Lopez Tijerina

Freedom Fighter-Alianza

Dolores Huerta

United Farm Workers Co-Founder

-Came to support 26 Day Fast 4 Education

Richard Aoki, **Yuri Kochiyama**

Black Panther, Prison Abolitionist

K. Wayne Yang-Educator

I think of you

(from across this small space in time)

I think of you
not as my everything
not as my light
not as my beginning
nor as my ending

I think of you
as an equal
as light
as a beginning
without and ending

I walk with you
            not behind
            nor in front

I love you
and my passion
is not a sign a weakness
but my source of strength

I am now learning
to share one space with you
and I look forward
to creating with you
dreaming with you
laughing with you

crying with you
flying with you
running with you
ok even if were both not in our
old high school track
but still
walking a new pace
because I don't want to be
what I once was
I want to be me now
as you want to be you
growing
embracing today
even if pain would argue otherwise

My love
together
you and me
we share space
where the center
becomes the dwelling place of
two
creating something new
and that creation knows no boundaries

Together
you and me
we
are lights
shining
walking
hand-in-hand

learning to dance, cook, play ball
and many nameless things
that we'll create along the way

WE
two letters
"W" and "E"
quite far apart in the alphabet
by themselves
just as important
created by God
but together
"WE"
create(s) something new
and I embrace it's mystery
it's beauty
it's splendor
as I embrace you
my love, my confidante,
my compañera and friend
as I think of you
from across this small space in time

. . .

an intro to césar a. preciado-cruz (teolol)

It's been said that César A. Cruz is a renowned poet, educator and human rights activist. But the way he sees it, he's a little Mexican kid from Jalisco, México who is not afraid to take on the empire and laugh while doing so.

From marching 76 straight miles to hunger striking for 16 and 26 days, Mr. Cruz has dedicated his life to fighting injustice. His relentless drive and passion have touched the lives of many, and his writings have received praise from activists and scholars throughout the world. Author **Rodolfo Acuña** sees ***"César as one of the new martyrs of our people."*** Acclaimed author and activist **Luis Rodriguez** depicts César's writings as filled with ***"fierce insight and righteous rage."*** But Mr. Cruz shrugs off the accolades with a humble smile and a thought. "I'm not important; we're but seeds of social change. Our role is a simple one; 'To comfort the disturbed, and to disturb the comfortable.' (MLK quote) Nothing more, and nothing less!"

Mr. Cruz received his education in a rancho in Juchitlán, on the streets of Compton, East Los, as an undergraduate at UC Berkeley majoring in History, and of course just living life. He is a tireless education advocate and is never afraid to speak truth to power.

Mr. Cruz has been an educator for the last 14 years. In the past he opened his own Freedom School in Richmond, CA. called "Making Changes." In 2004 he received the "Peacemaker of the Year" Award from the California State Assembly but declined it because he feels that it is hypocritical to have peace without justice. Mr. Cruz also received the "Outstanding Commitment to Justice Award" from Pacifica Radio. Mr. Cruz travels throughout the year lecturing at various schools, universities, community centers and rallies while avoiding the policía and la migra. ¡¿Y qué!?

To reach Mr. Cruz please check out his website at www.CesarCruz.com Also to pick up multiple copies of this book please log on to:

www.**Revenge**Of**The**Illegal**Alien**.com